Snow White and the Seven Dwarfs

Retold by Sue Aren~

Illustrated by Sus~ ~ve

OXFORD
UNIVERSITY PRESS

Before you read, what do you know about the story?

1   A nasty king had a magic mirror.
    ☐ True   ☑ False

2   The mirror said that Snow White was more beautiful than the King.
    ☐ True   ☐ False

3   The Queen was very angry so she told a huntsman to take Snow White into the forest and kill her.
    ☐ True   ☐ False

4   The huntsman couldn't kill her so he told her to run away into the forest.
    ☐ True   ☐ False

5   Snow White lived with six dwarfs.
    ☐ True   ☐ False

6   When Snow White ate a piece of poisoned banana, she fell to the floor and the dwarfs thought that she was dead.
    ☐ True   ☐ False

7   The dwarfs put Snow White in a glass box and took her to the mountain.
    ☐ True   ☐ False

8   A prince saw Snow White and fell in love with her.
    ☐ True   ☐ False

9   The dwarfs dropped the box and the piece of banana fell out of her mouth.
    ☐ True   ☐ False

10 The Prince and the Princess were married and the Queen ran away.
    ☐ True   ☐ False

ONCE upon a time, on a cold winter's day, a queen sat by the window of her castle. She sat and made clothes for her baby. She wanted to have a little girl.

Sometimes she looked out of the window. Outside, the snow fell, and it was very cold.

Suddenly, she pricked her finger with her needle, and three drops of red blood fell from it.

'Red is a beautiful colour,' she thought.

Then she looked at the dark black wood of the trees outside and at the white snow.

'My little girl will be very beautiful,' thought the Queen. 'She will have skin as white as snow, hair as black as those trees and cheeks as red as blood.'

cheeks	needle	prick	skin
the sides of your face			our bodies are covered in skin

Soon the Queen had her baby, a little daughter. And the little girl had skin as white as snow, hair as black as trees in winter and cheeks as red as blood.

'Oh, dear little child,' said the Queen, 'you are very beautiful! I will call you Snow White.'
She loved the little girl very much. But when Snow White was only two years old, a very sad thing happened. The Queen was very ill and she died.

After a few years, Snow White's father, the King, married again. His new queen was beautiful, but she was also nasty and unkind. She thought that she was the most beautiful woman in the country. 'And I will *always* be the most beautiful woman in the country!' she said.

The new queen looked at Snow White. She saw that the little girl was very beautiful, and she was jealous. She saw the light in Snow White's eyes and she wanted to kill her.

jealous

when you are jealous, you want to have something which belongs to another person

The new queen had a magic mirror. Every day she stood in front of it and asked:

'Mirror, mirror, on the wall,
Who is the most beautiful of all?'
The mirror always answered:
'You are, Queen.'
But one day, when she asked this question, the mirror answered:
'Of all the women who stand tall,
You, Queen, are the most beautiful of all.
But listen now, for this is true:
Snow White is more beautiful than you.'

mirror .

a piece of glass
which you can
look in and see
yourself

The Queen was very angry.

'When I see Snow White, I am ill!' she said.

'She must die. I never want to see her face again.'

She gave some money to a huntsman and said to him, 'Take Snow White into the forest and kill her. Do this or you will die. Go! Be quick! Bring me back her heart. Then I will know that she is dead.'

The huntsman did not want to do it, but he was afraid. So he took Snow White and together they walked into the forest. He put his hand on his knife three times. But each time Snow White turned and looked at him, and he could not kill her.

forest	heart	huntsman	knife

1 Answer the questions.

1 On a cold winter's day, a queen sat and made ... for her baby.
a ☑ clothes   b ☐ a fire   c ☐ food

2 She wanted her daughter to be very ...
a ☐ clever   b ☐ kind   c ☐ beautiful

3 'She will have ... as white as snow,' she thought.
a ☐ cheeks   b ☐ hair   c ☐ skin

4 When her baby ..., she called her Snow White.
a ☐ died   b ☐ was born   c ☐ was ill

5 Her mother died when Snow White was only two ... old.
a ☐ days   b ☐ months   c ☐ years

6 After ... years, Snow White's father, the King, married again.
a ☐ a few   b ☐ five   c ☐ many

7 The new queen thought that she was the most beautiful woman in the ...
a ☐ country   b ☐ town   c ☐ world

8 The Queen was ... of Snow White because she was a very beautiful little girl.
a ☐ afraid   b ☐ jealous   c ☐ tired

9 Every day ... asked her magic mirror, 'Who is the most beautiful of all?'
a ☐ Snow White   b ☐ the King   c ☐ the Queen

10 ... the mirror answered, 'Snow White is more beautiful than you.'
a ☐ Every day   b ☐ One day   c ☐ Sometimes

2 Complete the sentences.

again   always   back   before   could   daughter   deer

~~forest~~   girl   must   on   over   will

The Queen   I want you to take Snow White into the
             1____forest____ and kill her.

Huntsman   Snow White? The King's 2_____? But
             she's only a little 3_____.

The Queen   When I see Snow White, I am ill! She
             4_____ die. I never want to see her face
             5_____. Kill her. Do this or you will
             die. Go! Be quick! Bring me 6_____ her
             heart. Then I 7_____ know that she is
             dead.

Snow White   Oh, thank you. I've 8_____ wanted to go
             into the forest.
             Snow White turned and looked at the hunts-
             man, and he 9_____ not kill her. They
             walked 10_____ into the forest. He put
             his hand on his knife again.
             Oh, and look 11_____ there! There's a
             little 12_____. Can you see it? Oh, and
             look at those flowers! I've never seen any like
             that 13_____. What are they?
             Snow White turned and looked at the huntsman
             again, and he could not kill her.

At last, the huntsman said, 'Listen, Snow White. The Queen said that I must kill you. But I can't do it. Run, Snow White! Run far away into the forest. And do not come back to the castle.'

Then the huntsman killed a deer and took its heart. 'I will take this deer's heart back to the Queen,' he thought. 'And I will tell her that Snow White is dead.'

Snow White was alone and lost. She ran through the forest.
She ran all day. Now it was late and she was afraid.

The forest was full of strange noises. She knew that there
were wild animals there, but they did not come near her.
At last, Snow White came out of the forest. She saw a
mountain, and at the foot of the mountain she saw a
little house.

lost

when you are
lost, you don't
know where
you are

wild animals

animals which
do not live with
people

'I'll go and knock on the door,' she thought. 'Then perhaps a kind person will help me.'

'Hello!' she called. But there was no answer. It was almost dark now, so she opened the door.

Inside, the furniture was very small, and there were seven of everything: seven little chairs and seven little beds. There were seven little cups on the table, and seven plates of food.

'Perhaps seven little children live here,' thought Snow White. 'But where are they?'

furniture

Snow White was very hungry, but she didn't want to take some-one's dinner. So she ate a little from each plate, and she drank a little from each cup. Then she went upstairs and fell asleep on three of the little beds.

The house belonged to seven dwarfs. Every day the dwarfs went to the mountain and looked for gold. That night they finished their work and came home.

'Someone has eaten from our plates and drunk from our cups,' said one.

'Perhaps it was a mouse,' laughed the others.

'Come on! Let's take off our boots and sit down to eat.'

Then the youngest dwarf called from upstairs, 'Come quickly, everybody. Come and see. There is a young girl asleep on our beds. She is very beautiful.'

boots   dwarf   mouse

a very small
man or woman

1 What happened to Snow White? Fill in the gaps.

afraid   and   ate   drank   fell   food   furniture   heard

into   knew   late   must   out of   ran   ~~run~~   strange   to

very   will

The huntsman told Snow White to [1]___run___ far away
[2]_____ the forest. So, she [3]_____ all day until it
was [4]_____ and she was [5]_____ . She
[6]_____ that there were wolves in the forest and she
[7]_____ other wild animals making [8]_____ noises.
She thought, 'If I stay in the forest, I [9]_____ die.
I [10]_____ get out of the forest.'
At last, she came [11]_____ the forest. She saw a little
house at the foot of a mountain. 'I'll go [12]_____ knock
on the door,' she thought. There was no one at home. Inside,
the [13]_____ was very small, and there were seven of
everything. There were seven cups on the table, and seven plates
of [14]_____ . Snow White was [15]_____ hungry, but
she didn't want [16]_____ take someone's dinner. So she
[17]_____ a little from each plate and she [18]_____ a
little from each cup. Then she went upstairs and [19]_____
asleep.

2 Look at the pictures and write the words.

1   She had skin _a s_
_w h i t e a s_ snow
and hair _a s b l a c k_
_a s_ trees in winter.

2   'She _m_ _ _ _ die. I
_n_ _ _ _ _ _ want to see
her face _a_ _ _ _ _ the
Queen said to the huntsman.

3   'Run _f_ _ _ _ _a_ _ _ _ _
into the forest. And do not come
_b_ _ _ _ _ to the castle,' said
the huntsman.

4   'I _w_ _ _ _ _ take
this deer's heart back to the
Queen and _t_ _ _ _ _ her
that Snow White is dead.'

5   'I'll go and knock on the door.
Then _p_ _ _ _ _ _ _ _
a kind person _w_ _ _ _ _help
me.'

6   'Someone _h_ _ _
_e_ _ _ _ _ _ from our
plates and _d_ _ _ _ _ _
from our cups.'

All the other dwarfs ran upstairs.
'Yes, she is very beautiful!' they
said. 'Shhh! Don't wake her.'
So that night they all slept
downstairs by the fire.
In the morning, Snow White
told them her story.
'Stay here with us,' said the
dwarfs. 'The Queen is a very
dangerous woman. You can never
go back to your castle now.'
'Yes,' said the oldest dwarf. 'Stay.
Please stay.'
'Thank you,' said Snow White.
'You are all very kind.'

So Snow White stayed and lived with the seven dwarfs. She cooked and cleaned and washed for them, and they were kind to her.

Every morning the dwarfs went to the mountain to look for gold.

'Be careful, Snow White,' they said when they left. 'The Queen is a very dangerous woman. She must not know that you are here. Don't leave the house and do not open the door to anyone.'

'The Queen will never find me,' said Snow White. 'She thinks that I am dead.'

The Queen did not speak to her magic mirror for a long time. But one day, she stood in front of it and asked:

'Mirror, mirror, on the wall,
Who is the most beautiful of all?'

And the mirror answered:

'You, Queen, are beautiful, it's true.
But there is one more beautiful than you.
Snow White's not dead, she's living still,
In a house in the forest over the hill.
And although you are beautiful, it's true,
Snow White is more beautiful than you.'

'What?' said the Queen. 'She's not dead? I'll kill the huntsman! And I'll kill Snow White too, when I find her.

Then the Queen dressed as an old woman. She put some ribbons in a basket and left the castle secretly. 'Snow White will not know that it's me,' she laughed.

She walked quickly through the forest until she came to the little house at the foot of the mountain. 'Hello,' she called. 'Is anyone in?' Snow White looked out of the window. 'What do you want?' she asked. 'Would you like to buy some ribbons, my dear?' said the old woman.

ribbons

secretly

if you do something secretly, nobody sees you do it

1 Read and circle.

The ¹horse /(house) belonged to seven dwarfs. ²Every / One day the dwarfs went to the mountain and looked ³for / at gold. ⁴At / That night they finished their ⁵work / walk and came home.

'Someone has eaten from our plates and ⁶drank / drunk from our cups,' said one.

'Perhaps it ⁷was / is a mouse,' laughed the ⁸others / other. Come on! Let's take ⁹out / off our ¹⁰books / boots and sit down and ¹¹read / eat. Then the ¹²younger / youngest dwarf called from ¹³upstairs / the stairs, 'Come quickly, everybody. ¹⁴Come /Run and see. There is a ¹⁵funny / young girl asleep ¹⁶on / in our beds. She is very beautiful.'

All the other dwarfs ¹⁷run / ran upstairs.

'Yes, she is ¹⁸very / nearly beautiful!' they said. 'Shhh! Don't ¹⁹wake / work her.' So that night they all ²⁰stopped / slept downstairs ²¹by the fire / out of fear.

In the morning, Snow White ²²told / sold them her story.

²³'Stop / Stay here with us,' said the dwarfs. 'The Queen is a ²⁴very / heavy dangerous woman. You can never go back to your castle ²⁵now / no.'

'Yes,' said the ²⁶older / oldest dwarf. 'Stay. Please stay.'

2 Complete the sentences then act the play.

anyone ~~careful~~ dangerous dead living more

most must than that when will Would

The Dwarfs	Be [1] _careful_ , Snow White. The Queen is a very [2]_____ woman. She [3]_____ not know that you are here. Don't leave the house. Do not open the door to [4]_____ . Be careful! Goodbye, Snow White.
Snow White	The Queen [5]_____ never find me. She thinks [6]_____ I am dead.
The Queen	Mirror, mirror, on the wall, Who is the [7]_____ beautiful of all?
The Mirror	You, Queen, are beautiful, it's true. But there is one [8]_____ beautiful than you. Snow White's not dead, she's [9]_____ still, In a house in the forest over the hill. And although you are beautiful, it's true, Snow White is more beautiful [10]_____ you.
The Queen	What? She's not [11]_____ ? I'll kill the huntsman! And I'll kill Snow White too, [12]_____ I find her.
The Queen	Hello. Is anyone in?
Snow White	What do you want?
The Queen	[13]_____ you like to buy some ribbons, my dear?

Snow White looked at the ribbons. They were beautiful ribbons, pink and blue and yellow.

'She's just a poor old woman,' thought Snow White.

'She can't hurt me.'

So she opened the door.

The old woman showed Snow White the ribbons.

'Look at these pink ones.'

'They're beautiful,' said Snow White.

'Here, I'll help you. I'll tie them for you.'

But the old woman tied the ribbons very tightly and Snow White could not breathe. She fell to the floor.

That night the dwarfs found her there. They saw the new ribbons and quickly untied them.

'What happened?' they asked.

Snow White told them about the old woman.

'That was not an old woman,' said the dwarfs. 'That was the Queen!'

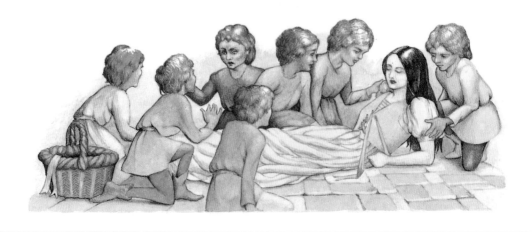

breathe	tie		tightly
to take in air and push it out again, through your mouth or nose	He's tying his shoe	He has untied his shoe	The ribbons are tied very tightly

Back at the castle, the Queen stood in front of her mirror and asked:

'Mirror, mirror, on the wall,

Who is the most beautiful of all?'

But again the mirror answered:

'You, Queen, are beautiful, it's true.

But there is one more beautiful than you.

Snow White's not dead, she's living still,

In a house in the forest over the hill.

And although you are beautiful, it's true,

Snow White is more beautiful than you.'

'What?' said the Queen. 'Is she still not dead? Then I will go to her again.'

So the Queen dressed as another old
woman. This time she put some
poisoned combs in her basket.
At the dwarfs' house she called,
'Good morning! I've got some combs.
Beautiful combs for your hair. Is anyone there?'

Snow White looked out of the window.
'I'm sorry, old woman,' she said, 'but you can't come into
the house.'
'Well, you can come to the door and look, can't you?' said
the old woman.
Snow White thought for a minute. She wanted to see the
combs very much.
'All right,' she said, and she went downstairs and opened
the door.

combs   poison

The old woman opened her basket and showed Snow White the poisoned combs.
'I like that pink comb,' said Snow White.
'Do you?' said the old woman. 'Here, my dear. I'll put it in your hair.'

Then she stuck the poisoned comb into Snow White's head and poor Snow White fell to the floor.

stuck
past tense of
stick: to push

1 What has happened? Write.

called couldn't died dressed drunk eaten gone

~~had~~ married stuck taken tied told tried

1 The Queen has ¹_____had_____ a baby, a little daughter
   ²_____ Snow White.

2 Snow White's mother has ³_____ and her father, the
   King, has ⁴_____ again. The new Queen is jealous of
   Snow White.

3 The huntsman has ⁵_____ Snow White into the forest
   to kill her. He has ⁶_____ to kill her, but he
   ⁷_____ do it. So he has ⁸_____ her to run far
   away into the forest.

4 Snow White has ⁹_____ to the dwarfs' house. She's
   ¹⁰_____ a little from each of their plates, ¹¹_____
   from each of their cups, and now she's fallen asleep on their beds.

5 The Queen has ¹²_____ as an old woman and gone to
   the dwarfs' house. She has ¹³_____ some ribbons very
   tightly and Snow White cannot breathe.

6 The Queen has gone back to the dwarfs' house. This time she
   has ¹⁴_____ a poisoned comb into Snow White's head.

2 Crossword.

4 ▶ a ... old woman

2 ▶

5 ▶

6 ▶

9 ▶

10 ▶

11 ▶

Down/Across clues shown in grid:

1 (down) m i r r o r

2 (across)

3 (down)

4 (across)

5 (across)

6 (across)

7 (down)

8 (down)

9 (across)

10 (across)

11 (across)

12 (across)

1 ▼

3 ▼

8 ▼ Snow White was more ... than the Queen.

7 ▼ 'Run ... away into the forest,' he said.

12 ▶

11 ▼ Her ... was as white as snow.

25

That night the dwarfs found her. They saw the comb and pulled it from her hair. 'What happened?' they asked. Snow White told them about the old woman. 'That was the Queen again!' said the oldest dwarf. 'Snow White, you must remember: do not open the door to anyone.' Back at the castle, the Queen stood before the magic mirror and asked:

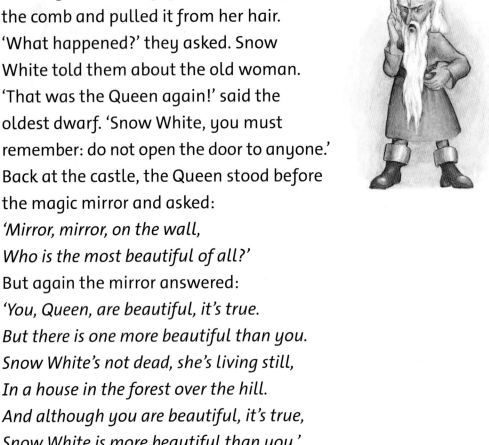

'Mirror, mirror, on the wall,
Who is the most beautiful of all?'
But again the mirror answered:
'You, Queen, are beautiful, it's true.
But there is one more beautiful than you.
Snow White's not dead, she's living still,
In a house in the forest over the hill.
And although you are beautiful, it's true,
Snow White is more beautiful than you.'
'Is she still alive?' said the Queen. 'Then I'll go to her again. I'll give her a poisoned apple.'

The Queen dressed as a farmer's wife and went to the
dwarfs' cottage. But Snow White did not want to open
the door.

'I'm sorry, old woman,' she called. 'You can't come in. The
dwarfs said that I must not open the door.'

Then the old woman showed her the poisoned apple.

'I'm sorry, old woman,' said Snow White. 'I haven't got
any money.'

'You don't have to buy it, dear,' said the old woman. 'I'll
give it to you for nothing.'

'Hm,' thought Snow White, 'the apple looks very nice.'

farmer

A farmer and
his wife

'Don't be afraid,' said the old woman. It's not poisoned. Look, I'll cut it in two. I'll eat this green half and you can have the beautiful red half. See? There's no danger.'

'All right,' said Snow White. 'Thank you, old woman.' And she took the red half and began to eat.

But when the first piece of the poisoned apple was in her mouth, she fell to the floor.

'Ha!' laughed the old woman. 'Goodbye for ever, Snow White.'

Back at the castle, the Queen asked her mirror:
'Mirror, mirror, on the wall,
Who is the most beautiful of all?'
And now at last the mirror answered:
'You are, Queen.'
That night, the dwarfs returned and found Snow White on
the floor. They tried to wake her but she did not move or
open her eyes.
'This time she is dead,' said the oldest dwarf. 'She has gone
from us for ever.'
For three days and nights the dwarfs sat by Snow White.
They knew that she was dead, but they did not want
to bury her.

bury
to put
something
under the
ground

1 Make sentences about the story.

1 The dwarfs said that Snow White

2 They also told her

3 The Queen stuck a poisoned comb into her head

4 When the dwarfs saw the comb,

5 The magic mirror told the Queen

6 'I'll go to her again

7 'You can't come in because the dwarfs said that

8 Snow White thought that

9 'I'll eat this half and

10 When the poisoned apple was in her mouth,

a not to open the door to anyone.

b and I'll give her a poisoned apple.'

c must not leave the house.

d and Snow White fell to the floor.

e you can have the beautiful red half.'

f the apple looked very nice.

g that Snow White was not dead.

h Snow White fell to the floor.

i they pulled it from her hair.

j I must not open the door.'

2 Answer the questions.

1 What happened when Snow White was two years old?
   The Queen, her mother, was very ill and died.

2 What did the Queen ask her mirror every day?
   _____

   _____

3 Why was the Queen very angry one day?
   _____

   _____

4 What did the Queen ask the huntsman to do?
   _____

   _____

5 Why did the huntsman want to take a deer's heart back to the Queen?
   _____

   _____

6 What did the dwarfs tell Snow White about opening the door?
   _____

   _____

7 Why do you think that Snow White opened the door to the Queen? What did she want to do? Did she know that it was the Queen?
   _____

   _____

8 Why did the dwarfs think that Snow White was dead?
   _____

   _____

'She looks as if she is only asleep,' they said.
'We can't bury her in the ground.'
So they made a glass box, put Snow White in it and
carried her up the mountain.
'She can lie here,' said the oldest dwarf. 'Then we can
come and see her every day.'

On the side of the box the dwarfs wrote in gold:
HERE LIES SNOW WHITE, THE DAUGHTER OF A KING
and one dwarf always sat with her, day and night.

Time went by, but Snow White's skin was still as white as snow. Her cheeks were still as red as blood and her hair was still as black as trees in winter.

Then one day, a prince came by with some friends. When he saw Snow White, he fell in love with her at once.

'I want to take her with me,' he said to the dwarf.

'I will give you anything!'

'No,' said the dwarf.

'Snow White belongs to us.'

But the Prince asked again and again.

'Can I take her with me? Please.'

At last, the dwarf said, 'Wait here. I will go and get my brothers.'

Then all the dwarfs came and stood in front of the Prince.

'I am in love with her,' said the Prince. 'I can't live without her.'

'Yes,' said the oldest dwarf. 'You love Snow White. I can see it in your face. And we must give her to you. You are a prince and she is a princess, the daughter of a king. We are only poor dwarfs.'

'Take all my gold,' said the Prince.

'No,' said the old dwarf. 'We don't want anything. We will give her to you because you love her.'

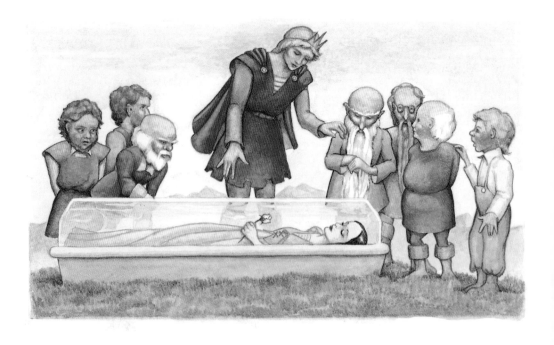

The dwarfs began to carry the glass box down the mountain. But they tripped near a tree and the box fell.
At that moment, the piece of apple fell out of Snow White's mouth.

She opened her eyes and saw the Prince. When she saw him, she fell in love with him at once.
'Here you see your husband,' said the Prince. 'Will you be my wife?'
'Yes,' she said.
So Snow White said goodbye to her friends the dwarfs, and went away with the Prince.

trip
to fall

In December they were married and there was a big party.
Lots of important people came, and one of these important
people was the jealous Queen.

When she saw Snow White, she couldn't believe her eyes.
'What is this?' she said. 'Is Snow White still alive?'

She was very angry. When she saw Snow White and the
Prince, she was jealous. She ran out of the castle and no one
saw her again.

Snow White loved the Prince, and he loved her. In time, they
had seven children, and they all lived happily ever after.

Order the words.

1   at once.   Snow White,   with her   he saw

     he fell in love   When

   When he saw Snow White, he fell in love with her at once.

2   to carry   The dwarfs   the glass box   down   began

     the mountain.

   _____

3   mouth.   of apple   At that moment,   Snow White's

     fell   the piece   out of

   _____

4   at once.   with him   the Prince,   in love   Snow White

     she saw   When   fell

   _____

5   Snow White,   couldn't   saw   When   her eyes.   she

     believe   the   Queen

   _____

6   ever after.   they all   seven children   They   lived   and

     had   happily

   _____

OXFORD
UNIVERSITY PRESS

Great Clarendon Street, Oxford OX2 6DP

Oxford University Press is a department of the University of Oxford.
It furthers the University's objective of excellence in research, scholarship,
and education by publishing worldwide in

Oxford New York

Auckland Cape Town Dar es Salaam Hong Kong Karachi
Kuala Lumpur Madrid Melbourne Mexico City Nairobi
New Delhi Shanghai Taipei Toronto

With offices in

Argentina Austria Brazil Chile Czech Republic France Greece
Guatemala Hungary Italy Japan Poland Portugal Singapore
South Korea Switzerland Thailand Turkey Ukraine Vietnam

OXFORD and OXFORD ENGLISH are registered trade marks of
Oxford University Press in the UK and in certain other countries

First published 2009
2017
11

ISBN: 978 0 19 4802611

Printed in China

ACKNOWLEDGEMENTS

Original story retold by: Sue Arengo
Illustrated by: Susan Rowe